TO _____

Disney's
SMALL WORLD LIBRARY
GOOFY AND THE GONDOLA
An Adventure in Italy

GROLIER ENTERPRISES INC.
DANBURY, CONNECTICUT

Developed by The Walt Disney Company in conjunction with Nancy Hall, Inc.
ISBN 0-7172-8215-5

"Gawrsh!" Goofy gasped as the cruise ship sailed toward Venice. "It's beautiful!"

Venice was the first stop on Mickey's and Goofy's vacation in Italy. The city rose like a fantastic dream out of the Adriatic Sea. The buildings seemed to float on the blue water.

Mickey looked up from his guidebook. "Look, Goofy, this is St. Mark's Square. What wonderful buildings!" he said, pointing to the dome of a big church. "That's one of the five domes of St. Mark's Church."

Then Mickey pointed out the tall watchtower and the pink marble Palace of the Doges, where the leaders of Venice used to live.

Mickey and Goofy couldn't wait to see more of Venice. "Let's take a gondola tour!" Mickey exclaimed.

Soon they were seated in one of the famous curved boats. The gondolier told them about the city as he poled the boat along the Grand Canal.

"Venice isn't just one island," the gondolier explained. "It's made of 120 small islands crisscrossed by bridges and canals."

After their tour, Mickey and Goofy visited an old toy shop called Antonio's. While the owner proudly showed a marionette to Mickey, his son Carlo showed Goofy a hand-carved toy gondola.

"Gawrsh, that's pretty!" exclaimed Goofy. "That would be a great present for Mickey." But when Goofy saw the price tag, he had to turn Carlo down.

Discouraged that Goofy didn't buy the gondola, Carlo slipped out of the store and sadly sat on the front steps.

Goofy, who felt badly that he couldn't buy the gondola, went outside and sat down next to the boy.

"Do you like helping your father in his store?" Goofy asked Carlo.

"Oh, yes," the boy answered. "But right now I only work one day a week. I would like to come here every day after school, but my father thinks I am too young. And maybe he is right. After all, if I were a good salesperson, you would have bought that toy gondola."

"Gawrsh, I wish I could afford it!" Goofy exclaimed. "It would be the perfect gift for my friend Mickey. He's always doing nice things for me, but whenever I try to buy Mickey a present, or throw him a party, or anything, it turns out to be a big mess."

"I'd have to work all vacation to pay for that gondola,"
Goofy sighed. "And how could I get a job here when I
don't know anyone?"

Carlo thought for a moment, then his face brightened.

"Maybe I can help you," he volunteered. "What kind
of job would you like?"

Goofy decided that he would really like to be a gondolier. He ran inside the store to tell Mickey that he was going to take a walk with Carlo. Then Carlo and Goofy went down to the canal, where Carlo knew one of the men in the black pants, striped shirts, and ribboned hats.

"Carlo!" the gondolier cried. "You helped me pick out a lovely doll for my little girl. If you want me to give your friend a job, I most certainly will. Can you start right away?" he asked Goofy.

"I sure can!" Goofy replied.

Goofy climbed into the gondola. He jabbed the heavy pole into the water and pushed, but the boat went nowhere. "Gawrsh!" Goofy exclaimed. "Being a gondolier isn't as easy as it looks."

Then he shoved the pole with all his might. The gondola shot backward and Goofy flew forward.

Goofy landed on an ice-cream cart on the famous Rialto Bridge.

"You've ruined my gelato!" shouted Luigi, the ice-cream vendor.

When Luigi saw Carlo running towards Goofy, he calmed down. "You are the boy who showed me how to put my son's model train set together. I want to thank you again for all your help," he said gratefully.

When Carlo explained that his friend Goofy needed a job, Luigi shook Goofy's gooey hand.

"Any friend of Carlo's is a friend of mine," he declared. "You can clean up here and take over my gelato cart today. It will be nice to have the afternoon off."

Carlo decided to go for a walk while Goofy worked at the gelato cart.

"Gawrsh, what a great job!" Goofy said as he served his first customer a delicious cone of gelato.

"This ice cream is so good," Goofy thought. "I bet I could make a fortune selling it by gondola all through Venice. I'd ring a bell and people would come running to buy Goofy's Gelato!"

Goofy was so busy daydreaming that he forgot to close the lid to the cart. By the time Luigi and his son came by for some gelato, the sun had melted it all!

"You've turned my gelato into soup!" Luigi fumed. "You're fired! If you weren't a friend of Carlo's. . ."

As Goofy walked away dejectedly, a man approached him. "You are a friend of Carlo's? I am Marco, the fisherman."

Marco shook Goofy's hand. "Carlo is one of my best friends. Every Christmas he helps me find just the right toys for my nieces and nephews. If you need a job, you've got one. Can you start first thing in the morning?"

"You bet!" said Goofy enthusiastically.

The next morning Goofy got up early to start his new job. Before he left, he wrote Mickey a note that said, "Went to meet a friend. See you tonight."

Soon Goofy was delivering fish for Marco. He rode along with the crates in the barge, then jumped on shore to carry fish to stores and restaurants.

Goofy was doing fine until a hungry cat rubbed against his leg. Goofy tripped and fell face-first into a crate of fish. What a mess!

Just then Carlo walked by. "Marco said you were here," he said. "I guess this job isn't working out very well, either."

"I can't do anything right," Goofy complained. "I always seem to mess everything up."

"Don't give up," said Carlo. "My father says that when things go wrong, you should only try harder."

"But now you seem tired and hungry," Carlo observed.
"I know just the thing to perk you up."

Carlo brought Goofy to his favorite pizzeria. Goofy
watched the master chef toss pizza dough.

"I'd like to do that!" Goofy said enthusiastically.

Carlo was glad to see Goofy so interested in a new job.
He hurried to the kitchen to talk to the restaurant owner.

"You are the boy who fixed my little daughter's broken doll for free!" the owner said, when he saw Carlo. "Of course I will give your friend a job."

And with that, Goofy found himself wearing a chef's hat and apron. He began to toss a big blob of pizza dough.

Meanwhile, Mickey was surprised to discover that Goofy had gone off without him. Mickey decided to spend the day on the nearby islands of Burano and Murano.

Mickey took the water bus to Burano, where he saw women making traditional lace patterns by hand. On Murano, men blew molten glass into fantastic vases, glasses, and figurines. Mickey had a wonderful time, but he wished Goofy had come with him.

"Goofy has been acting strangely," Mickey thought to himself. "I wonder what's wrong."

Then Mickey had a wonderful idea. "I know just the thing to cheer Goofy up!" he said.

When Mickey got back to Venice, he went straight to the toy store to buy Goofy a present.

"Goofy liked a toy he saw in this store," Mickey thought as he walked into Antonio's Toy Shop.

While Mickey paid for the toy, Antonio asked, "My son was meeting your friend today. Do you know where they went? It's getting late, and I'm beginning to get worried."

Mickey told Antonio he didn't know where Goofy and Carlo had gone. He and Antonio decided they would go look for the two.

"Let's check the places Carlo likes to visit," Antonio said. "He's a good boy. He wouldn't go very far without my permission."

"Carlo!" Antonio said, seeing his son at a table in the front of the restaurant. "I thought you might be here."

"Where is Goofy?" Mickey asked. Then he looked up, and there was Goofy tossing a pizza way up in the air.

Goofy was so surprised to see Mickey, he forgot what he was doing. The wet, sticky dough came down and landed all over his face.

"What are you doing?" Mickey asked Goofy in a concerned voice. "Where have you been all day?"

Goofy sighed as he tried to remove the pizza dough from his face. He didn't want to ruin the surprise for Mickey, but he also didn't want Mickey to worry.

"Gawrsh, Mickey," Goofy said. "I was only trying to earn enough money to buy that toy gondola for you."

"You mean this one?" Mickey asked, opening the package.

"Gawrsh, how could you afford it?" Goofy gasped in amazement. "That toy costs thousands of lira."

Mickey laughed as he explained. "You should have read the guidebook, Goofy. Money isn't the same everywhere. Three thousand lira isn't a lot of money. In fact, it's not much money at all."

Mickey wasn't the only one who wanted to know what was going on. Antonio was amazed when he found out how his son had spent the past two days.

"You must know a lot about business to have gotten Goofy all those jobs," Antonio observed proudly. Then he put his arm around his son's shoulders. "I missed you today—and so did all the customers. Maybe it's time to make you my partner."

The next day, Mickey and Goofy visited the toy store. Carlo played with the marionettes in the window and entertained the tourists walking by. Many people hurried into the store to buy toys.

"I worked so many jobs, and I still don't have a present for you," Goofy sighed sadly.

"It's the thought that counts, Goofy," Mickey said. "And the important thing is that you meant well and you tried hard."

ANTONIO & SON
Toy Shop

Goofy smiled and shrugged sheepishly. "It was kind of fun trying to do all those jobs. And I sure got to learn a lot about Venice!"

Did You Know...?

There are many different customs and places that make each country special. Do you remember some of the things below from the story?

The canals of Venice are its "roads." They carry many kinds of boats, including not only gondolas and motorboats, but also ferry boats, garbage boats, boats selling food, and even ambulance boats.

Venice has more than 400 bridges. Perhaps the most famous is the Bridge of Sighs. This bridge got its name from the sighs of prisoners who once passed over it as they traveled from jail to face trial.

St. Mark's Cathedral in St. Mark's Square took centuries to build. Inside it is decorated with brilliant mosaics and other beautiful works of art.

Pizza comes originally from the south of Italy but now is sold all over the country. In Naples, it has a thin crust that can be folded in half. Sicilian pizza is very thick and topped with onions. In Genoa, pizza is topped with garlic, black olives, and tiny fish called anchovies.

Glassmaking in Europe was first developed in Venice around 1300. Glassblowers on the island of Murano spend many years learning their craft. They are said to be the finest glassblowers in the world.

Italians love ice cream, which they call *gelato* (ja-LA-toe). There are many different flavors to buy from special carts in the streets.

Puppet shows are a favorite entertainment for Italian children. Italian puppets and marionettes are often handmade and beautiful works of art. *Pinocchio*, the famous story about a marionette, was written by an Italian author named Carlo Collodi.

Fishing is an important occupation along Italy's coast.
Italian fishermen catch sardines, anchovies, clams, and
squid. Squid is a favorite food, especially fried and eaten
with lemon juice or a spicy sauce.

Ciao (chow) is what Italians say to each other when
meeting or parting.
Come sta? (kom-ma STA) means "How are you?"
Grazie (GRAT-zee) means "Thank you."